# RUNNER'S WORLD
## TRAINING DIARY

**NAME:**

_____

**ADDRESS:**

_____

**JOURNAL FOR THE YEAR**

_____TO_____

# RUNNER'S WORLD

# TRAINING DIARY

**A daily dose of motivation, training
tips, and running wisdom for
every kind of runner – from
weekend joggers to competitive racers**

By the editors of **Runner's World** magazine
with an introduction by Amby Burfoot

## REVISED AND UPDATED

NATMAGRODALE

NATMAGRODALE

# CONTENTS

# INTRODUCTION

When my running friends discover my vast trove of training diaries (40 years' worth) on a dusty bookshelf, they can rarely suppress their laughter. You see, I have obsessive tendencies. There, I said it. Admitting it is the first step, right?

One training diary page explains how I once ran 60 x 200-metre repeats on an indoor track. It was February, as I recall, and a good time to be indoors. The workout wasn't actually as hard as it might sound. After the first half-dozen repeats, I got into a groove, a trance of sorts. The next 50 passed like a dream.

When I had injuries, my diary entries switched gears, turning to desperate attempts at rehabilitation. A throbbing Achilles tendon just about drove me to madness. I had a big race coming up – big, as in a 54-mile-long ultramarathon – and my swollen Achilles wouldn't even permit a short hobble. I decided masochism must be the answer, icing the afflicted area once an hour, followed each time by squeezing the tendon as hard as I could. This was roughly the equivalent of hitting myself on the thumb with a hammer. Amazingly, it worked. I was able to finish the ultramarathon.

A runner's training diary, like the one in your hands, has many potential uses. You can scribble in the margins, as I sometimes did, to explicate the infinite – and sometimes infinitely silly – details of your life. Or you can distil your thoughts and actions first, giving more focus and perhaps more meaning. Since you are a runner, you will no doubt use this diary primarily to record various aspects of your running. Here are four great areas to consider for your daily notes. Any one of them alone can help make you a better, healthier runner. Combine a few, and you'll have enough power to take your running to a whole new level.

**MOTIVATION.** A training diary should motivate you to run more, or at least more regularly. Indeed, published medical studies have shown that exercise logs are one of the few proven ways to stick to your goals. Look at those yawning, empty pages. They just beg to be filled in. Don't let them go hungry.

**NUTRITION.** Training diaries are useful for planning and keeping track of how you fuel your body for runs and what foods work best in helping you achieve your running goals. Most runners want to combine a good diet with a consistent exercise programme. After all, it doesn't make much sense to run 20 miles a week and then undo all the health benefits of a regular aerobic-training programme by eating burgers and fries at every meal.

**TRAINING AND RACING.** Now we've reached the heart of the training diary, the reason you're using one in the first place – to record and analyse your daily, weekly, and yearly training and racing achievements. As you look back over your diary to analyse what worked and what didn't, keep these key principles in mind: **(1)** Your training should increase gradually for 6-16 weeks before major races, particularly before marathons. **(2)** Even these 'build-ups' should include easy days and often easy weeks. **(3)** You should taper for 1-3 weeks before a big race. **(4)** You need at least two recovery periods during the year, often during the worst summer heat and during the end-of-year Christmas party season, when you dramatically decrease your training for 2-4 weeks. And lastly, **(5)** you should plan new and different training/ racing goals every year to stay fresh and motivated.

**INJURY PREVENTION.** Runners get injured. That's the bad news. The good news: Most of these injuries are minor muscle and tendon strains that heal quickly if you let them. Repeat: if you let them. So the first rule of injury prevention is always to take 2-4 days off from running at the onset of any running-related pains. You can walk, swim (or pool jog), or perhaps ride your bike. But don't run. The old aphorism 'A stitch in time saves nine' applies perfectly to running. Beyond appropriate days off, use ice to limit inflammation, stretch gently after workouts (but not before – a thorough warm-up is a much better idea), and do strengthening exercises to build balanced leg muscles. Keep track of your injuries and your methods for rehabbing them in your diary so you can refer to it should that injury crop up again.

By Amby Burfoot

*Editor-at-large*, Runner's World *magazine,*
*winner of the Boston Marathon*

## HOW TO USE THIS DIARY

There's no right or wrong way to use this book. The goal here is to record the information you'll need to help you improve your running and to remember what worked and what didn't work.

We've provided a template in which you can write down the things most runners have found useful to record. On this page, you'll see what a sample week of training looked ▶

### MONDAY
ROUTE: Parkway
DISTANCE: **5 miles**                    TIME: **40:06**
NOTES: tired after Sun. race

CROSS-TRAINING: lifted before work

### TUESDAY
ROUTE: Trilogy
DISTANCE: **2.7 miles**                    TIME: untimed
NOTES: should do more speed work—felt great

CROSS-TRAINING:

### WEDNESDAY
ROUTE:
DISTANCE:                    TIME:
NOTES:

REST DAY

CROSS-TRAINING:

### THURSDAY
ROUTE: Parkway—ran w/Trish
DISTANCE: **6.2**                    TIME: **51:37**
NOTES: running w/people is the best thing for me to do

CROSS-TRAINING: Lifted

### FRIDAY
ROUTE: Thompson Loop
DISTANCE: **3.5 miles**                    TIME: 27:12
NOTES: eat bigger breakfast, swim was great—tired now

CROSS-TRAINING: swam 1,500 before work

## SATURDAY

ROUTE: **Luke's long run**

DISTANCE: **10 miles**                    TIME: **1:22**

NOTES: **best long run of the year so far, bring more water**

CROSS-TRAINING:

## SUNDAY

ROUTE: **track workout**

DISTANCE: **10x800**                    TIME: **@3:15 on 2:00 rest**

NOTES: **felt v. strong on both—good week! Crispy legs after track**

CROSS-TRAINING: **hiked w/Annie in p.m.**

### NOTES

◄ like for one of our editors. If you have regular runs you complete, give the routes names and use them as a form of shorthand.

We strongly suggest that even if you record nothing else, be sure to put down your distance or time and how you felt. Also, do weekly summations. It will make analysing your data that much easier at the end of the year.

And one more thing: Have fun!

| WEEKLY TOTAL |
|:---:|
| **32.4** |

| TOTAL MILEAGE TO DATE |
|:---:|
| **337 + 32.4 = 369.4** |

## TIP OF THE WEEK

Even on slow days, warm up to stay comfortable. Adapt to an increased workload by walking for about three minutes and then slowly jogging. A proper warm-up should leave you feeling strong and comfortable by mid run, and it reduces your risk of injury.

"Running is the classic road to self-consciousness, self-awareness, and self-reliance. Independence is the outstanding characteristic of the runner. He learns the harsh reality of his physical and mental limitations."

**Noël Carroll, philosopher**

### MONDAY
ROUTE:

DISTANCE:                    TIME:

NOTES:

CROSS-TRAINING:

### TUESDAY
ROUTE:

DISTANCE:                    TIME:

NOTES:

CROSS-TRAINING:

### WEDNESDAY
ROUTE:

DISTANCE:                    TIME:

NOTES:

CROSS-TRAINING:

### THURSDAY
ROUTE:

DISTANCE:                    TIME:

NOTES:

CROSS-TRAINING:

### FRIDAY
ROUTE:

DISTANCE:                    TIME:

NOTES:

CROSS-TRAINING:

## SATURDAY

ROUTE:

DISTANCE:                    TIME:

NOTES:

CROSS-TRAINING:

## SUNDAY

ROUTE:

DISTANCE:                    TIME:

NOTES:

CROSS-TRAINING:

## NOTES

# NUTRITION

### USE FRUIT FOR ENERGY
· · · · · ·
If you can't get your hands on an energy bar, simply raid the fruit bowl. The natural sugars found in virtually all fruit are quickly processed by your body, giving you the extra energy you need to perform well on your next run. A banana 30 minutes before you set off is ideal.

### WEEKLY TOTAL

_____

### TOTAL MILEAGE TO DATE

_____

## TIP OF THE WEEK

Hit a training wall? Do speed work to up the pace. Once a week, run some measured segments 20-30 seconds per mile faster than your goal pace. For 5K and 10K runners, start with 400-metre repeats. Try some 800-metre repeats if you're a half-marathoners. Go for mile repeats if you are a marathoner. Repeats mean you run the distance several times, always at the same pace. Unlike intervals you don't have a set recovery time, you recover after each segment for long enough to repeat it at the same pace.

"The will to win means nothing if you haven't the will to prepare."

**Juma Ikangaa,**
**winner of eight**
**international marathons**

### MONDAY
ROUTE:

DISTANCE:                    TIME:

NOTES:


CROSS-TRAINING:

### TUESDAY
ROUTE:

DISTANCE:                    TIME:

NOTES:


CROSS-TRAINING:

### WEDNESDAY
ROUTE:

DISTANCE:                    TIME:

NOTES:


CROSS-TRAINING:

### THURSDAY
ROUTE:

DISTANCE:                    TIME:

NOTES:


CROSS-TRAINING:

### FRIDAY
ROUTE:

DISTANCE:                    TIME:

NOTES:


CROSS-TRAINING:

## SATURDAY

ROUTE:

DISTANCE:                    TIME:

NOTES:

CROSS-TRAINING:

## SUNDAY

ROUTE:

DISTANCE:                    TIME:

NOTES:

CROSS-TRAINING:

## NOTES

# NUTRITION

## FUELLING UP
. . . . . . .

Small, frequent meals help training performance. Make sure you're never too full by eating four or five small meals a day. Never skip breakfast before a lunch run, because your glycogen reserves will be too low. Going for a long time without eating also slows your metabolism.

### WEEKLY TOTAL

### TOTAL MILEAGE TO DATE

## TIP OF THE WEEK

Don't skip the cool-down on slow days. Even if you only went out for a casual run, blood can still pool in your legs and cause cramps if you don't cool down. Alternate 30-60 seconds of slow jogging with the same amount of walking for a total of 5 minutes; then walk the final 5 minutes.

"In running, it doesn't matter whether you come in first, in the middle, or last. You can say, 'I have finished.' There is a lot of satisfaction in that."

**Fred Lebow, founder of the New York Marathon**

### MONDAY
ROUTE:

DISTANCE:                    TIME:

NOTES:


CROSS-TRAINING:

### TUESDAY
ROUTE:

DISTANCE:                    TIME:

NOTES:


CROSS-TRAINING:

### WEDNESDAY
ROUTE:

DISTANCE:                    TIME:

NOTES:


CROSS-TRAINING:

### THURSDAY
ROUTE:

DISTANCE:                    TIME:

NOTES:


CROSS-TRAINING:

### FRIDAY
ROUTE:

DISTANCE:                    TIME:

NOTES:


CROSS-TRAINING:

## SATURDAY

ROUTE:

DISTANCE:             TIME:

NOTES:

CROSS-TRAINING:

## SUNDAY

ROUTE:

DISTANCE:             TIME:

NOTES:

CROSS-TRAINING:

## NOTES

# NUTRITION
## THE DARK SIDE
· · · · · ·

For a boost of beta-carotene and lutein, both great antioxidants, eat dark salad leaves like lamb's lettuce or kale. They're also a good source of potassium, magnesium and calcium. Use these leaves as a side salad or main dish topped with grilled chicken, beef, fish, or tofu.

### WEEKLY TOTAL

_____

### TOTAL MILEAGE TO DATE

_____

# WEEK 4

## TIP OF THE WEEK

Want to breathe deep? Keep your torso tall. Having a straight, upright posture promotes optimal lung capacity and stride length. If you start to slouch during a run, take a deep breath and feel yourself naturally straighten. As you exhale, simply maintain that upright position.

"We are different, in essence, from other men. If you want to win something, run 100 metres. If you want to experience something, run a marathon."

**Emil Zatopek, four-times Olympic gold medallist**

### MONDAY
ROUTE:

DISTANCE:                    TIME:

NOTES:

CROSS-TRAINING:

### TUESDAY
ROUTE:

DISTANCE:                    TIME:

NOTES:

CROSS-TRAINING:

### WEDNESDAY
ROUTE:

DISTANCE:                    TIME:

NOTES:

CROSS-TRAINING:

### THURSDAY
ROUTE:

DISTANCE:                    TIME:

NOTES:

CROSS-TRAINING:

### FRIDAY
ROUTE:

DISTANCE:                    TIME:

NOTES:

CROSS-TRAINING:

## SATURDAY

ROUTE:

DISTANCE: TIME:

NOTES:

CROSS-TRAINING:

## SUNDAY

ROUTE:

DISTANCE: TIME:

NOTES:

CROSS-TRAINING:

## NOTES

# NUTRITION

## FISH FOR COMPLIMENTS
· · · · · · ·

Pick the best type of salmon for your body – and your bank balance. Wild salmon contains much lower levels of chemicals than farm-raised salmon, but it can be pricey. A better option? Try out some tinned wild Alaskan salmon is less expensive but it's just as rich in healthy omega-3 fats.

## WEEKLY TOTAL

## TOTAL MILEAGE TO DATE

## TIP OF THE WEEK

Try this easy way to determine your effort level without investing in a heart monitor: Notice how often you breathe in relation to how many steps you are taking. Three or four strides for every inhale – you're running at a warm-up pace. Two strides per inhale and exhale – a good pace for long runs and races. When you're taking two strides when you breathe in and only one when you breathe out, you're at tempo run pace.

"Get going. Get up and walk if you have to, but finish the damned race."

**Ron Hill, in 1970 became first man to break the 2:10 barrier in the marathon**

### MONDAY
ROUTE:

DISTANCE:                    TIME:

NOTES:

CROSS-TRAINING:

### TUESDAY
ROUTE:

DISTANCE:                    TIME:

NOTES:

CROSS-TRAINING:

### WEDNESDAY
ROUTE:

DISTANCE:                    TIME:

NOTES:

CROSS-TRAINING:

### THURSDAY
ROUTE:

DISTANCE:                    TIME:

NOTES:

CROSS-TRAINING:

### FRIDAY
ROUTE:

DISTANCE:                    TIME:

NOTES:

CROSS-TRAINING:

## SATURDAY

ROUTE:

DISTANCE:                TIME:

NOTES:

CROSS-TRAINING:

## SUNDAY

ROUTE:

DISTANCE:                TIME:

NOTES:

CROSS-TRAINING:

## NOTES

# TRAINING

## MORNING MONITOR

Overtraining is the leading cause of running injury and burnout. To stay on pace – not above – monitor your morning heart rate for a week to get a baseline. Take your pulse every morning, and take a half-mileage day whenever it's more than 5 percent above baseline. Take the day off if it's more than 10 percent.

### WEEKLY TOTAL

### TOTAL MILEAGE TO DATE

# WEEK 6

WEEK OF _____ TO _____

## TIP OF THE WEEK

The best way to improve endurance is to lengthen your long run. Slow down your pace to about two-minutes-per-mile slower than your goal pace, and you can increase your endurance by an additional mile or two per long run. Do this every other weekend.

"I prefer to remain in blissful ignorance of the opposition. That way I'm not frightened by anyone's reputation."

**Ian Thompson, Commonwealth Games marathon gold medallist**

### MONDAY
ROUTE:

DISTANCE:                    TIME:

NOTES:

CROSS-TRAINING:

### TUESDAY
ROUTE:

DISTANCE:                    TIME:

NOTES:

CROSS-TRAINING:

### WEDNESDAY
ROUTE:

DISTANCE:                    TIME:

NOTES:

CROSS-TRAINING:

### THURSDAY
ROUTE:

DISTANCE:                    TIME:

NOTES:

CROSS-TRAINING:

### FRIDAY
ROUTE:

DISTANCE:                    TIME:

NOTES:

CROSS-TRAINING:

## SATURDAY

ROUTE:

DISTANCE:                    TIME:

NOTES:

CROSS-TRAINING:

## SUNDAY

ROUTE:

DISTANCE:                    TIME:

NOTES:

CROSS-TRAINING:

## NOTES

# NUTRITION

### MORNING BOOST

A breakfast protein shake will help power you through your day. Try this recipe before you leave for work: two eggs, a banana, a glass of skimmed milk, whey powder, and chocolate sauce for flavour. This should keep you going through a lunchtime run.

| WEEKLY TOTAL |
| --- |
| |

| TOTAL MILEAGE TO DATE |
| --- |
| |

# WEEK 7

WEEK OF _____ TO _____

## TIP OF THE WEEK

To boost your endurance and drastically increase strength, run hilly routes. Hills are almost as effective as track interval training for boosting aerobic power and far more effective at building strength. A good hill should take you at least a minute to charge. Look for a course with gradual downhills to prevent injury.

"Big occasions and races which have been eagerly anticipated almost to the point of dread are where great deeds can be accomplished."

**Jack Lovelock, Olympic 1500m gold medallist**

### MONDAY

ROUTE:

DISTANCE:                    TIME:

NOTES:

CROSS-TRAINING:

### TUESDAY

ROUTE:

DISTANCE:                    TIME:

NOTES:

CROSS-TRAINING:

### WEDNESDAY

ROUTE:

DISTANCE:                    TIME:

NOTES:

CROSS-TRAINING:

### THURSDAY

ROUTE:

DISTANCE:                    TIME:

NOTES:

CROSS-TRAINING:

### FRIDAY

ROUTE:

DISTANCE:                    TIME:

NOTES:

CROSS-TRAINING:

## SATURDAY

ROUTE:

DISTANCE:                    TIME:

NOTES:

CROSS-TRAINING:

## SUNDAY

ROUTE:

DISTANCE:                    TIME:

NOTES:

CROSS-TRAINING:

## NOTES

# TRAINING
## LIKE
## CLOCKWORK
· · · · · · ·

To get into the mind frame of running every day, make sure to run at the same time every day. If it's built into your schedule, you're less likely to skip a run – and more likely to look forward to the next day's workout if you do miss a day.

### WEEKLY TOTAL

_____

### TOTAL MILEAGE TO DATE

_____

# WEEK 8

## TIP OF THE WEEK

Switch shoes to relieve lower-body stress. A certain shoe can put undue stress on one area, so alternate the shoes you run in every other workout or so. If there's a particular style you like, just switch a new pair with a slightly more worn pair.

"A journey of 1,000 miles begins with a single step."

**Confucius, philosopher**

### MONDAY
ROUTE:

DISTANCE:                TIME:

NOTES:


CROSS-TRAINING:

### TUESDAY
ROUTE:

DISTANCE:                TIME:

NOTES:


CROSS-TRAINING:

### WEDNESDAY
ROUTE:

DISTANCE:                TIME:

NOTES:


CROSS-TRAINING:

### THURSDAY
ROUTE:

DISTANCE:                TIME:

NOTES:


CROSS-TRAINING:

### FRIDAY
ROUTE:

DISTANCE:                TIME:

NOTES:


CROSS-TRAINING:

## SATURDAY

ROUTE:

DISTANCE:                              TIME:

NOTES:

CROSS-TRAINING:

## SUNDAY

ROUTE:

DISTANCE:                              TIME:

NOTES:

CROSS-TRAINING:

## NOTES

# TRAINING

## EASE ANXIETY
· · · · · · ·
Relax before a workout or race by forcing yourself not to overthink it until the hour arrives. Otherwise, you'll build up anxiety. And if you run it over in your head too much, you won't be so flexible if something happens to stray from your plan.

### WEEKLY TOTAL

_____

### TOTAL MILEAGE TO DATE

_____

## TIP OF THE WEEK

Run faster with less effort – and correct your posture on and off the track – by swapping your desk chair for a stability ball. A stability ball strengthens your abdomen, lower back, and hips, which helps with better form and fewer injuries. Start with an hour a day, and gradually increase the time you spend on the ball.

"In this age, which believes there is a shortcut to everything, the greatest lesson to be learned is that the most difficult way is, in the long run, the easiest."

**Henry Miller, author**

### MONDAY
ROUTE:

DISTANCE:                          TIME:

NOTES:

CROSS-TRAINING:

### TUESDAY
ROUTE:

DISTANCE:                          TIME:

NOTES:

CROSS-TRAINING:

### WEDNESDAY
ROUTE:

DISTANCE:                          TIME:

NOTES:

CROSS-TRAINING:

### THURSDAY
ROUTE:

DISTANCE:                          TIME:

NOTES:

CROSS-TRAINING:

### FRIDAY
ROUTE:

DISTANCE:                          TIME:

NOTES:

CROSS-TRAINING:

## SATURDAY

ROUTE:

DISTANCE:                          TIME:

NOTES:

CROSS-TRAINING:

## SUNDAY

ROUTE:

DISTANCE:                          TIME:

NOTES:

CROSS-TRAINING:

## NOTES

# NUTRITION

## HOLD YOUR WATER

Replenish water and salt to keep going the distance. To keep your body moving during runs of 100 minutes or longer, down a high-sodium product like Lucozade Sport Body Fuel drink or chomp on PowerBar's Energize C2Max beforehand. The extra salts in them will help to keep you hydrated.

### WEEKLY TOTAL

### TOTAL MILEAGE TO DATE

## TIP OF THE WEEK

To adapt to the pace you're planning for race day, lengthen your work and rest intervals. Start with five reps of three minutes hard, two minutes easy, and over several weeks work your way up to two reps of 20 minutes hard, five minutes easy.

"Life begets life. Energy creates energy. It is by spending oneself that one becomes rich."

**Sarah Bernhardt, actress**

### MONDAY
ROUTE:

DISTANCE:                    TIME:

NOTES:

CROSS-TRAINING:

### TUESDAY
ROUTE:

DISTANCE:                    TIME:

NOTES:

CROSS-TRAINING:

### WEDNESDAY
ROUTE:

DISTANCE:                    TIME:

NOTES:

CROSS-TRAINING:

### THURSDAY
ROUTE:

DISTANCE:                    TIME:

NOTES:

CROSS-TRAINING:

### FRIDAY
ROUTE:

DISTANCE:                    TIME:

NOTES:

CROSS-TRAINING:

## SATURDAY

ROUTE:

DISTANCE:                    TIME:

NOTES:

CROSS-TRAINING:

## SUNDAY

ROUTE:

DISTANCE:                    TIME:

NOTES:

CROSS-TRAINING:

## NOTES

# NUTRITION

## GOT CALCIUM?

Make sure you're getting the full benefit of your calcium supplement by taking it at night instead of in the morning. More than 500mg of calcium consumed at once hampers absorption, and most likely your breakfast already gives you an ample dose from milk or calcium-fortified orange juice.

## WEEKLY TOTAL

_____

## TOTAL MILEAGE TO DATE

_____

## TIP OF THE WEEK

Keep a steady leg turnover for a steady pace. As you fatigue, your turnover slows before stride length diminishes. Unfortunately, leg turnover is what has the most impact on speed. When you notice yourself slowing, shorten your stride and quicken your turnover.

"I was 12 when I started and 34 before I achieved my dream, that should give people hope."

**Dame Kelly Holmes, double Olympic gold medallist**

### MONDAY
ROUTE:

DISTANCE:                    TIME:

NOTES:

CROSS-TRAINING:

### TUESDAY
ROUTE:

DISTANCE:                    TIME:

NOTES:

CROSS-TRAINING:

### WEDNESDAY
ROUTE:

DISTANCE:                    TIME:

NOTES:

CROSS-TRAINING:

### THURSDAY
ROUTE:

DISTANCE:                    TIME:

NOTES:

CROSS-TRAINING:

### FRIDAY
ROUTE:

DISTANCE:                    TIME:

NOTES:

CROSS-TRAINING:

## SATURDAY
ROUTE:

DISTANCE:                    TIME:

NOTES:

CROSS-TRAINING:

## SUNDAY
ROUTE:

DISTANCE:                    TIME:

NOTES:

CROSS-TRAINING:

## NOTES

# TRAINING
## SAVE YOUR SKIN
. . . . . . .
Apply sunblock under a T-shirt during sunny runs. A T-shirt has an SPF of about 7 and won't prevent sunburn. So slather on the high SPF an hour before your run, or look out for high-tech clothing that has built-in sun protection.

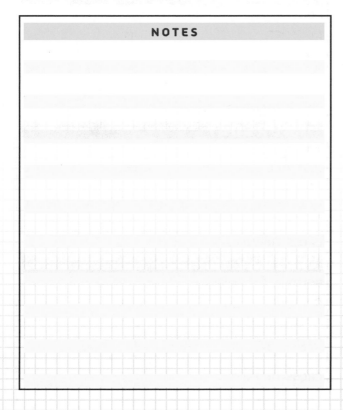

### WEEKLY TOTAL

### TOTAL MILEAGE TO DATE

# WEEK 12

WEEK OF _____ TO _____

## TIP OF THE WEEK

To stay cool on hot runs, hit the park instead of pounding the pavement. Hard surfaces can retain a lot of heat, and weaving around in the shade beneath the trees will also help you keep cool on your run.

"Pressure is nothing more than the shadow of great opportunity."

**Michael Johnson, four-times Olympic gold medallist**

### MONDAY
ROUTE:

DISTANCE:                     TIME:

NOTES:


CROSS-TRAINING:

### TUESDAY
ROUTE:

DISTANCE:                     TIME:

NOTES:


CROSS-TRAINING:

### WEDNESDAY
ROUTE:

DISTANCE:                     TIME:

NOTES:


CROSS-TRAINING:

### THURSDAY
ROUTE:

DISTANCE:                     TIME:

NOTES:


CROSS-TRAINING:

### FRIDAY
ROUTE:

DISTANCE:                     TIME:

NOTES:


CROSS-TRAINING:

## SATURDAY
ROUTE:
DISTANCE:                    TIME:
NOTES:

CROSS-TRAINING:

## SUNDAY
ROUTE:
DISTANCE:                    TIME:
NOTES:

CROSS-TRAINING:

## NOTES

# NUTRITION

### CHOCOLATE POWER
. . . . . .
Recovering from a tough workout is about replenishing lost glycogen stores. Chocolate milk does the trick just as well as a sports drink. For fewer calories, go for a low-fat variety, or make it yourself with skimmed milk and chocolate sauce.

### WEEKLY TOTAL
_____

### TOTAL MILEAGE TO DATE
_____

## TIP OF THE WEEK

Practice 5K racing through the off-season. You'll maintain racing fitness during the winter with this workout: warm up as you would before a race. Run half a kilometre at just-below 5K race pace, then run at race pace for another half kilometre. Note the time, and then jog for three to five minutes. Do enough one kilometre segments to complete the total race distance.

"If I am still standing at the end of the race, hit me with a board and knock me down, because that means I didn't run hard enough."

**Steve Jones, winner of four international marathons**

### MONDAY
ROUTE:

DISTANCE:                    TIME:

NOTES:


CROSS-TRAINING:

### TUESDAY
ROUTE:

DISTANCE:                    TIME:

NOTES:


CROSS-TRAINING:

### WEDNESDAY
ROUTE:

DISTANCE:                    TIME:

NOTES:


CROSS-TRAINING:

### THURSDAY
ROUTE:

DISTANCE:                    TIME:

NOTES:


CROSS-TRAINING:

### FRIDAY
ROUTE:

DISTANCE:                    TIME:

NOTES:


CROSS-TRAINING:

## SATURDAY
ROUTE:

DISTANCE:                    TIME:

NOTES:

CROSS-TRAINING:

## SUNDAY
ROUTE:

DISTANCE:                    TIME:

NOTES:

CROSS-TRAINING:

## NOTES

# TRAINING

### CROSS-TRAINING
• • • • • • •

Build rock-hard abs — and keep your heart rate up — with this tip: do crunches during the downtime between weight-lifting sets. It's also an easy way to condense your workout time.

### WEEKLY TOTAL

### TOTAL MILEAGE TO DATE

## TIP OF THE WEEK

Keep hydrated: before you race, learn what liquids your body needs. Don't mess with hydration on race day. Practise with the sports drink available on the course. Find out how frequently the route has aid stations and drink at that rate. Also, try a variety of bars and gels on long runs to see which settles best in your stomach.

"There is no better stage for heroism than a marathon."

**Dr George Sheehan, best-selling running author**

### MONDAY
ROUTE:

DISTANCE:               TIME:

NOTES:

CROSS-TRAINING:

### TUESDAY
ROUTE:

DISTANCE:               TIME:

NOTES:

CROSS-TRAINING:

### WEDNESDAY
ROUTE:

DISTANCE:               TIME:

NOTES:

CROSS-TRAINING:

### THURSDAY
ROUTE:

DISTANCE:               TIME:

NOTES:

CROSS-TRAINING:

### FRIDAY
ROUTE:

DISTANCE:               TIME:

NOTES:

CROSS-TRAINING:

## SATURDAY

ROUTE:

DISTANCE:                    TIME:

NOTES:

CROSS-TRAINING:

## SUNDAY

ROUTE:

DISTANCE:                    TIME:

NOTES:

CROSS-TRAINING:

## NOTES

# NUTRITION

## GO RAW!
. . . . . . .
Vitamin C and folic acid, two of the body's most vital nutrients, are partially destroyed by heat. So, eat red and orange peppers (packed with vitamin C) and leafy greens (a good source of folic acid) uncooked for a big nutritional hit.

**WEEKLY TOTAL**

_____

**TOTAL MILEAGE TO DATE**

_____

## TIP OF THE WEEK

To reduce muscle friction and run smoother, try dynamic flexibility training, a type of stretching that mimics the way your body actually moves while it is running. Here are two simple moves.

**Leg swings** With your left hand on a wall, stand on your right foot and swing your left leg back and forth in a kicking motion. Complete 10 swings and repeat with your right leg.

**Arm swings** Swing your right arm in a giant circle to loosen up the upper body. Repeat with your left arm.

"Most mistakes in a race are made in the first two minutes, perhaps in the very first minute."

**Jack Daniels, leading US running coach**

### MONDAY
ROUTE:

DISTANCE:                    TIME:

NOTES:

CROSS-TRAINING:

### TUESDAY
ROUTE:

DISTANCE:                    TIME:

NOTES:

CROSS-TRAINING:

### WEDNESDAY
ROUTE:

DISTANCE:                    TIME:

NOTES:

CROSS-TRAINING:

### THURSDAY
ROUTE:

DISTANCE:                    TIME:

NOTES:

CROSS-TRAINING:

### FRIDAY
ROUTE:

DISTANCE:                    TIME:

NOTES:

CROSS-TRAINING:

## SATURDAY

ROUTE:

DISTANCE:               TIME:

NOTES:

CROSS-TRAINING:

## SUNDAY

ROUTE:

DISTANCE:               TIME:

NOTES:

CROSS-TRAINING:

## NOTES

# TRAINING

## ZZZ FOR COLDS

Sleep soundly to stay healthy. Growth hormones that help to boost immunity are released during sleep, so keep colds at bay with eight hours of sleep every night, and more after a long run.

### WEEKLY TOTAL

### TOTAL MILEAGE TO DATE

## TIP OF THE WEEK

If dark days have you feeling low, try exercising early. Morning exercise can have the same effect as bright light. It can even readjust sleep/wake cycles of people with seasonal affective disorder. Wake up with a natural light alarm clock and you'll feel even feistier.

"You have to forget your last marathon before you try another. Your mind can't know what's coming."

**Frank Shorter, Olympic marathon gold medallist**

### MONDAY
ROUTE:

DISTANCE:                          TIME:

NOTES:

CROSS-TRAINING:

### TUESDAY
ROUTE:

DISTANCE:                          TIME:

NOTES:

CROSS-TRAINING:

### WEDNESDAY
ROUTE:

DISTANCE:                          TIME:

NOTES:

CROSS-TRAINING:

### THURSDAY
ROUTE:

DISTANCE:                          TIME:

NOTES:

CROSS-TRAINING:

### FRIDAY
ROUTE:

DISTANCE:                          TIME:

NOTES:

CROSS-TRAINING:

## SATURDAY

ROUTE:

DISTANCE:                    TIME:

NOTES:

CROSS-TRAINING:

## SUNDAY

ROUTE:

DISTANCE:                    TIME:

NOTES:

CROSS-TRAINING:

## NOTES

# NUTRITION

## PROTEIN POWER
· · · · · ·

To repair muscle fibres damaged during strength training, eat lean protein sources. Fat-free dairy and soy products, fish, lean beef, poultry, and eggs all supply needed amino acid. Aim for 80g of protein per day.

### WEEKLY TOTAL

### TOTAL MILEAGE TO DATE

# WEEK 17

WEEK OF _____ TO_____

## TIP OF THE WEEK

To strengthen your glutes, hamstrings, and quads – the muscles you need for leg turnover and running hills – try a walking lunge. Here's how: Stand straight, feet together. Take a long step forward, bend both knees, and lower your back knee to the floor. Stop when your forward knee is above your toe. Rise, bring your feet together, and repeat with the opposite leg. Continue for 15 to 20 paces. Add this into your regular training twice a week.

"At the two-thirds mark, I think of those who are still with me. Who might make a break? Should I? Then I give it all I've got."

**Ibrahim Hussein, winner of seven international marathons**

### MONDAY
ROUTE:

DISTANCE:                    TIME:

NOTES:

CROSS-TRAINING:

### TUESDAY
ROUTE:

DISTANCE:                    TIME:

NOTES:

CROSS-TRAINING:

### WEDNESDAY
ROUTE:

DISTANCE:                    TIME:

NOTES:

CROSS-TRAINING:

### THURSDAY
ROUTE:

DISTANCE:                    TIME:

NOTES:

CROSS-TRAINING:

### FRIDAY
ROUTE:

DISTANCE:                    TIME:

NOTES:

CROSS-TRAINING:

## SATURDAY

ROUTE:

DISTANCE:                    TIME:

NOTES:

CROSS-TRAINING:

## SUNDAY

ROUTE:

DISTANCE:                    TIME:

NOTES:

CROSS-TRAINING:

## NOTES

# TRAINING

### EASE THE PAIN
· · · · · · ·

Does your head hurt after you run but only for a few minutes? It's called an exertional headache. Either scale back your training, or take ibuprofen before exercising.

### WEEKLY TOTAL

### TOTAL MILEAGE TO DATE

## TIP OF THE WEEK

Improve your cardiovascular functioning by climbing stairs. Because your foot spends more time in the push-off phase, you're training the primary muscles used for running at a greater intensity. Added bonus: all the benefits of hill running but easier on your joints.

### MONDAY
ROUTE:

DISTANCE:                    TIME:

NOTES:

CROSS-TRAINING:

### TUESDAY
ROUTE:

DISTANCE:                    TIME:

NOTES:

CROSS-TRAINING:

### WEDNESDAY
ROUTE:

DISTANCE:                    TIME:

NOTES:

CROSS-TRAINING:

### THURSDAY
ROUTE:

DISTANCE:                    TIME:

NOTES:

CROSS-TRAINING:

### FRIDAY
ROUTE:

DISTANCE:                    TIME:

NOTES:

CROSS-TRAINING:

## SATURDAY
ROUTE:

DISTANCE:                    TIME:

NOTES:

CROSS-TRAINING:

## SUNDAY
ROUTE:

DISTANCE:                    TIME:

NOTES:

CROSS-TRAINING:

## NOTES

# NUTRITION
## SLOW DOWN
Eat slowly to lose weight. For your body to register that it's full, you need to wait 20 minutes. To avoid extra calories from speed-eating, take time to finish each bite and converse more at the table. It'll help you enjoy the meal more, too.

"I became a great runner because if you're a kid in Leeds and your name is Sebastian you've got to become a great runner."

**Sebastian Coe, double Olympic 1500m gold medallist**

### WEEKLY TOTAL

### TOTAL MILEAGE TO DATE

# WEEK 19

**WEEK OF** _____ TO _____

## TIP OF THE WEEK

Drop PR times with speed work. To keep the spinal cord's fast-running cells from deteriorating, there's only one thing to do: run fast. Without sprints – we're talking less than 800 metres – these cells deteriorate as you get older, slowing you down. Do one speed session a week of repeats between 100 and 300 meters in length. Use minimal recovery time, around 100 meters, or whatever you can handle.

"Anyone can run 20 miles. It's the next six that count."

**Barry Magee, winner of the Fukuoka Marathon, Japan**

### MONDAY

ROUTE:

DISTANCE:                         TIME:

NOTES:

CROSS-TRAINING:

### TUESDAY

ROUTE:

DISTANCE:                         TIME:

NOTES:

CROSS-TRAINING:

### WEDNESDAY

ROUTE:

DISTANCE:                         TIME:

NOTES:

CROSS-TRAINING:

### THURSDAY

ROUTE:

DISTANCE:                         TIME:

NOTES:

CROSS-TRAINING:

### FRIDAY

ROUTE:

DISTANCE:                         TIME:

NOTES:

CROSS-TRAINING:

## SATURDAY

ROUTE:

DISTANCE:                    TIME:

NOTES:

CROSS-TRAINING:

## SUNDAY

ROUTE:

DISTANCE:                    TIME:

NOTES:

CROSS-TRAINING:

## NOTES

# NUTRITION

## HYDRATE FOR A HEALTHY HEART
· · · · · · ·
Lower your risk of heart disease by up to 60 percent by hydrating properly. Drink five or more 250ml glasses of water a day for optimum results, more if you're working out strenuously or in hot weather.

**WEEKLY TOTAL**

_____

**TOTAL MILEAGE TO DATE**

_____

## TIP OF THE WEEK

Improve running economy with a hop, skip, and jump. To consume less oxygen when working hard – and thereby be able to work longer or preserve your effort for later – add plyometric drills once or twice a week. These controlled forms of jumping and skipping also improve the 'explosive' power of your muscles.

"Don't quit, dammit!"

**Marty Liquori, US middle-distance runner**

### MONDAY
ROUTE:

DISTANCE:                    TIME:

NOTES:

CROSS-TRAINING:

### TUESDAY
ROUTE:

DISTANCE:                    TIME:

NOTES:

CROSS-TRAINING:

### WEDNESDAY
ROUTE:

DISTANCE:                    TIME:

NOTES:

CROSS-TRAINING:

### THURSDAY
ROUTE:

DISTANCE:                    TIME:

NOTES:

CROSS-TRAINING:

### FRIDAY
ROUTE:

DISTANCE:                    TIME:

NOTES:

CROSS-TRAINING:

## SATURDAY

ROUTE:

DISTANCE:                    TIME:

NOTES:

CROSS-TRAINING:

## SUNDAY

ROUTE:

DISTANCE:                    TIME:

NOTES:

CROSS-TRAINING:

## NOTES

# NUTRITION

## AN APPLE A DAY

······

If you're always buying punnets of fruit, only to forget about them and find them going off in the fridge days later, get into the habit of putting some on your cereal each morning. It'll be an excellent first step towards getting your five a day – and will ensure that you get more value out of your shopping.

## WEEKLY TOTAL

_____

## TOTAL MILEAGE TO DATE

_____

# WEEK 21

**WEEK OF** _____ TO _____

## MONDAY
ROUTE:

DISTANCE:                          TIME:

NOTES:


CROSS-TRAINING:

## TUESDAY
ROUTE:

DISTANCE:                          TIME:

NOTES:


CROSS-TRAINING:

## WEDNESDAY
ROUTE:

DISTANCE:                          TIME:

NOTES:


CROSS-TRAINING:

## THURSDAY
ROUTE:

DISTANCE:                          TIME:

NOTES:


CROSS-TRAINING:

## FRIDAY
ROUTE:

DISTANCE:                          TIME:

NOTES:


CROSS-TRAINING:

## SATURDAY

ROUTE:

DISTANCE:                    TIME:

NOTES:

CROSS-TRAINING:

## SUNDAY

ROUTE:

DISTANCE:                    TIME:

NOTES:

CROSS-TRAINING:

## NOTES

# NUTRITION

## DO NOT DISTURB
········

Make sure you get your daily dose of fibre – 25g per day for women and 38g for men. But don't eat a fibre-rich meal under three hours before your run, or you could have problems with your digestion. Pre-race stick to foods with no more than 5g to avoid the risk of an upset stomach.

## WEEKLY TOTAL

_____

## TOTAL MILEAGE TO DATE

_____

## TIP OF THE WEEK

Keep your calf muscles balanced by running the opposite way around your usual route every other day. Undue pressure is constantly put on one side of the body if you always run in the same direction. It's even more important to do this if you are running on a track.

"I always loved running... it was something you could do by yourself, and under your own power. You could go in any direction, fast or slow as you wanted, fighting the wind if you felt like it, seeking out new sights just on the strength of your feet and the courage of your lungs."

**Jesse Owens, quadruple Olympic gold medallist**

### MONDAY
ROUTE:

DISTANCE:                TIME:

NOTES:

CROSS-TRAINING:

### TUESDAY
ROUTE:

DISTANCE:                TIME:

NOTES:

CROSS-TRAINING:

### WEDNESDAY
ROUTE:

DISTANCE:                TIME:

NOTES:

CROSS-TRAINING:

### THURSDAY
ROUTE:

DISTANCE:                TIME:

NOTES:

CROSS-TRAINING:

### FRIDAY
ROUTE:

DISTANCE:                TIME:

NOTES:

CROSS-TRAINING:

## SATURDAY

ROUTE:

DISTANCE:                              TIME:

NOTES:

CROSS-TRAINING:

## SUNDAY

ROUTE:

DISTANCE:                              TIME:

NOTES:

CROSS-TRAINING:

## NOTES

# TRAINING

### TAKE IT EASY
. . . . . . .

Recurrent injuries? Take it easier. If you always seem to get injured just when you're getting really fit, it means you haven't let yourself fully adapt to the new schedule. Back off by 10-20 percent of your weekly mileage for at least a month. If you still develop injuries at this lower level, back off again. It'll be frustrating, but not as frustrating as getting hurt and not being able to run at all.

### WEEKLY TOTAL

_____

### TOTAL MILEAGE TO DATE

_____

## TIP OF THE WEEK

Use on-and-off intervals to keep pace in check. If you overexert yourself in the middle of a race, only to die way before the finish line, on-and-off intervals can teach you how to slow yourself down. Run 400 metres at 10K race pace, followed by another 400 metres 10 seconds slower. Alternate back and forth for 2K. Take five minutes' recovery, and repeat for another 2K.

"When I came to New York in 1978, I was a full-time schoolteacher and track runner and determined to retire from competitive running. But winning the New York City Marathon kept me running for another decade."

**Grete Waitz, World Championship marathon gold medallist**

### MONDAY
ROUTE:

DISTANCE:                          TIME:

NOTES:

CROSS-TRAINING:

### TUESDAY
ROUTE:

DISTANCE:                          TIME:

NOTES:

CROSS-TRAINING:

### WEDNESDAY
ROUTE:

DISTANCE:                          TIME:

NOTES:

CROSS-TRAINING:

### THURSDAY
ROUTE:

DISTANCE:                          TIME:

NOTES:

CROSS-TRAINING:

### FRIDAY
ROUTE:

DISTANCE:                          TIME:

NOTES:

CROSS-TRAINING:

## SATURDAY

ROUTE:

DISTANCE:                    TIME:

NOTES:

CROSS-TRAINING:

## SUNDAY

ROUTE:

DISTANCE:                    TIME:

NOTES:

CROSS-TRAINING:

## NOTES

# TRAINING

### SHOULDER THE BURDEN
· · · · · · ·

Stopping shoulder cramp is as easy as noting form at the end of a run. Once you're tired, the tendency is for the shoulders to rise up. When you notice this, drop your arms to your sides, and gently shake them as you forcefully exhale.

### WEEKLY TOTAL

### TOTAL MILEAGE TO DATE

## TIP OF THE WEEK

Since running combined with the ravages of time can cause your muscles to tighten, try doing Pilates, which stretches and strengthens the core. Pilates helps increase strength and flexibility, and your form won't fall apart when you get tired.

"I was unable to walk for a whole week after that, so much did the race take out of me. But it was the most pleasant exhaustion I have ever known."

**Emil Zatopek on winning the marathon at the Helsinki Olympics in 1952**

### MONDAY
ROUTE:

DISTANCE:                    TIME:

NOTES:

CROSS-TRAINING:

### TUESDAY
ROUTE:

DISTANCE:                    TIME:

NOTES:

CROSS-TRAINING:

### WEDNESDAY
ROUTE:

DISTANCE:                    TIME:

NOTES:

CROSS-TRAINING:

### THURSDAY
ROUTE:

DISTANCE:                    TIME:

NOTES:

CROSS-TRAINING:

### FRIDAY
ROUTE:

DISTANCE:                    TIME:

NOTES:

CROSS-TRAINING:

## SATURDAY

ROUTE:

DISTANCE:                    TIME:

NOTES:

CROSS-TRAINING:

## SUNDAY

ROUTE:

DISTANCE:                    TIME:

NOTES:

CROSS-TRAINING:

## NOTES

# NUTRITION

## COMEBACK MUM

Rebound slowly after childbirth. Even though you'll want to get right back into running, prevent getting overfatigued by easing into it after pregnancy. Space a full 48 hours between runs – and be patient.

### WEEKLY TOTAL

_____

### TOTAL MILEAGE TO DATE

_____

## TIP OF THE WEEK

If your running partner talks too much for your taste, hit the country trails to cool the chatter without risking hurting your friendship. A challenging single-track makes conversation very difficult and changes the pace of your workout.

"I just run as hard as I can for 20 miles, and then race."

**Steve Jones, winner of four international marathons**

### MONDAY
ROUTE:

DISTANCE:                TIME:

NOTES:

CROSS-TRAINING:

### TUESDAY
ROUTE:

DISTANCE:                TIME:

NOTES:

CROSS-TRAINING:

### WEDNESDAY
ROUTE:

DISTANCE:                TIME:

NOTES:

CROSS-TRAINING:

### THURSDAY
ROUTE:

DISTANCE:                TIME:

NOTES:

CROSS-TRAINING:

### FRIDAY
ROUTE:

DISTANCE:                TIME:

NOTES:

CROSS-TRAINING:

## SATURDAY

ROUTE:

DISTANCE:                    TIME:

NOTES:

CROSS-TRAINING:

## SUNDAY

ROUTE:

DISTANCE:                    TIME:

NOTES:

CROSS-TRAINING:

## NOTES

# TRAINING

### HIATUS
· · · · · · ·

To enjoy running more, take a short holiday from it. For a psychological break from training and to regenerate your adrenal system, take a week off. That's right, a whole week. Don't exercise at all for two or three days, then do light cross-training the rest of the week.

### WEEKLY TOTAL

### TOTAL MILEAGE TO DATE

# WEEK 26

## TIP OF THE WEEK

Get your energy back with post-marathon snacking. Restock your spent glycogen stores by eating a 200- to 300-calorie snack within half an hour of finishing. The snack should be 80 percent carbs and 20 percent protein. A protein bar and some sports drink will do the trick.

### MONDAY
ROUTE:

DISTANCE:                    TIME:

NOTES:

CROSS-TRAINING:

### TUESDAY
ROUTE:

DISTANCE:                    TIME:

NOTES:

CROSS-TRAINING:

### WEDNESDAY
ROUTE:

DISTANCE:                    TIME:

NOTES:

CROSS-TRAINING:

### THURSDAY
ROUTE:

DISTANCE:                    TIME:

NOTES:

CROSS-TRAINING:

### FRIDAY
ROUTE:

DISTANCE:                    TIME:

NOTES:

CROSS-TRAINING:

## SATURDAY
ROUTE:

DISTANCE:                    TIME:

NOTES:

CROSS-TRAINING:

## SUNDAY
ROUTE:

DISTANCE:                    TIME:

NOTES:

CROSS-TRAINING:

## NOTES

# TRAINING
## BEGINNING RUNNING
· · · · · ·
If you're injury-prone, run every other day to give your body time to repair and rebuild. Forty-eight hours allows for complete recovery.

"You know who I look up to? I look up to the five-minute milers. Because they don't get any of the good things I get. They're out there running just as hard. They're the guys with guts, the guys with a lot of inner determination."

**Mark Belger, US middle distance runner**

### WEEKLY TOTAL

_____

### TOTAL MILEAGE TO DATE

_____

## TIP OF THE WEEK

During marathon training, prepare your mind – and body – to work while exhausted: Add speed at the end of a long run. If you're doing a 20 mile run, do your easy long-run pace for most of it, then, with eight miles to go, begin running one minute per mile slower than your marathon goal pace. Speed up every 2 miles to run the last couple of miles at goal pace or slightly faster.

"It's very hard to understand in the beginning that the whole idea is not to beat the other runners. Eventually you learn that the competition is against the little voice inside you that wants to quit."

**George Sheehan, best-selling running author**

### MONDAY
ROUTE:

DISTANCE:                    TIME:

NOTES:


CROSS-TRAINING:

### TUESDAY
ROUTE:

DISTANCE:                    TIME:

NOTES:


CROSS-TRAINING:

### WEDNESDAY
ROUTE:

DISTANCE:                    TIME:

NOTES:


CROSS-TRAINING:

### THURSDAY
ROUTE:

DISTANCE:                    TIME:

NOTES:


CROSS-TRAINING:

### FRIDAY
ROUTE:

DISTANCE:                    TIME:

NOTES:


CROSS-TRAINING:

## SATURDAY

ROUTE:

DISTANCE:                    TIME:

NOTES:

CROSS-TRAINING:

## SUNDAY

ROUTE:

DISTANCE:                    TIME:

NOTES:

CROSS-TRAINING:

## NOTES

# NUTRITION

## GET FRESH

Up your vegetable intake by buying the freshest produce you can find. Because it tastes better, you'll likely to eat more of it. Try shopping at your local farmer's market whenever possible.

### WEEKLY TOTAL

_____

### TOTAL MILEAGE TO DATE

_____

## TIP OF THE WEEK

Do you sometimes get a pain in your upper abdomen when running that goes away once you stop? It's a side stitch, which is a cramp in the diaphragm that happens when blood supply is low. Slow down for 30 seconds. If the pain is on the right side, exhale each time your left foot hits the ground, and vice versa. Also, practise slow, deep 'belly breathing.'

"My thoughts before a big race are usually pretty simple. I tell myself: 'Get out of the blocks, run your race, stay relaxed. If you run your race, you'll win....' Channel your energy. Focus."

**Carl Lewis, nine-times Olympic track and field gold medallist**

### MONDAY
ROUTE:

DISTANCE:                    TIME:

NOTES:



CROSS-TRAINING:

### TUESDAY
ROUTE:

DISTANCE:                    TIME:

NOTES:



CROSS-TRAINING:

### WEDNESDAY
ROUTE:

DISTANCE:                    TIME:

NOTES:



CROSS-TRAINING:

### THURSDAY
ROUTE:

DISTANCE:                    TIME:

NOTES:



CROSS-TRAINING:

### FRIDAY
ROUTE:

DISTANCE:                    TIME:

NOTES:



CROSS-TRAINING:

## SATURDAY

ROUTE:

DISTANCE:                    TIME:

NOTES:

CROSS-TRAINING:

## SUNDAY

ROUTE:

DISTANCE:                    TIME:

NOTES:

CROSS-TRAINING:

## NOTES

# NUTRITION

## BLAST BELLY FAT WITH DAIRY
· · · · · · ·
Losing abdominal fat (lowering your chances of diabetes and heart disease) is easier when you consume enough calcium. It's not a magic weight-loss cure, since losing pounds ultimately depends on cutting calories, but dairy might speed up your metabolism and seems to slow down fat-cell formation.

### WEEKLY TOTAL

_____

### TOTAL MILEAGE TO DATE

_____

# WEEK 29

WEEK OF _____ TO_____

## TIP OF THE WEEK

If you want a quick fix for wasted energy, try to relax by concentrating on keeping your neck loose as you run. If you do this your shoulders and back usually follow suit and you'll run more efficiently.

"I was pushed by myself because I have my own rule, and that is that every day I run faster, and try harder."

**Wilson Kipketer, triple World Championship 800m gold medallist**

### MONDAY
ROUTE:

DISTANCE:                              TIME:

NOTES:

CROSS-TRAINING:

### TUESDAY
ROUTE:

DISTANCE:                              TIME:

NOTES:

CROSS-TRAINING:

### WEDNESDAY
ROUTE:

DISTANCE:                              TIME:

NOTES:

CROSS-TRAINING:

### THURSDAY
ROUTE:

DISTANCE:                              TIME:

NOTES:

CROSS-TRAINING:

### FRIDAY
ROUTE:

DISTANCE:                              TIME:

NOTES:

CROSS-TRAINING:

## SATURDAY

ROUTE:

DISTANCE:                    TIME:

NOTES:

CROSS-TRAINING:

## SUNDAY

ROUTE:

DISTANCE:                    TIME:

NOTES:

CROSS-TRAINING:

## NOTES

# TRAINING

## HEED HEADPHONE ETIQUETTE
......

To stay safe on the road, wear some headphones that let in noise, and don't crank the volume all the way up. Since headphones are banned in many races, it might be a good idea to use them only in the gym.

### WEEKLY TOTAL

_____

### TOTAL MILEAGE TO DATE

_____

## TIP OF THE WEEK

Don't let a recently recovered injury keep you running tentatively. If a doctor has given you the go-ahead, what's holding you back is probably mental. Avoid injury anxiety through relaxation and focus. Zero in on small details, such as your pace or form, to distract your mind from negative thoughts about the old injury.

"We run, not because we think it is doing us good, but because we cannot help ourselves. The more restricted our society and work become, the more necessary it will be to find some outlet for this craving for freedom. No one can say, 'You must not run faster than this, or jump higher than that.' The human spirit is indomitable."

**Roger Bannister, first to run a four-minute mile**

### MONDAY
ROUTE:

DISTANCE:                              TIME:

NOTES:

CROSS-TRAINING:

### TUESDAY
ROUTE:

DISTANCE:                              TIME:

NOTES:

CROSS-TRAINING:

### WEDNESDAY
ROUTE:

DISTANCE:                              TIME:

NOTES:

CROSS-TRAINING:

### THURSDAY
ROUTE:

DISTANCE:                              TIME:

NOTES:

CROSS-TRAINING:

### FRIDAY
ROUTE:

DISTANCE:                              TIME:

NOTES:

CROSS-TRAINING:

## SATURDAY
ROUTE:

DISTANCE:                    TIME:

NOTES:


CROSS-TRAINING:

## SUNDAY
ROUTE:

DISTANCE:                    TIME:

NOTES:


CROSS-TRAINING:

## NOTES

# TRAINING

### TIGHT HAMSTRINGS?
· · · · · · ·
Stretch on a bench or stairs to target just the right muscles. Place your leg on the top of a bench or the third stair and lean your chest forward. Move your leg up a stair to deepen the stretch.

### WEEKLY TOTAL
_____

### TOTAL MILEAGE TO DATE
_____

## TIP OF THE WEEK

Reduce pounding on your legs by running only on soft surfaces – trails, dirt, and grass. However, road racers should still do some road running to stay used to hard surfaces.

"The decathlon is nine Mickey Mouse events and the 1500 metres."

**Steve Ovett, Olympic 800m gold medallist**

### MONDAY
ROUTE:

DISTANCE:                    TIME:

NOTES:


CROSS-TRAINING:

### TUESDAY
ROUTE:

DISTANCE:                    TIME:

NOTES:


CROSS-TRAINING:

### WEDNESDAY
ROUTE:

DISTANCE:                    TIME:

NOTES:


CROSS-TRAINING:

### THURSDAY
ROUTE:

DISTANCE:                    TIME:

NOTES:


CROSS-TRAINING:

### FRIDAY
ROUTE:

DISTANCE:                    TIME:

NOTES:


CROSS-TRAINING:

## SATURDAY

ROUTE:

DISTANCE:                   TIME:

NOTES:

CROSS-TRAINING:

## SUNDAY

ROUTE:

DISTANCE:                   TIME:

NOTES:

CROSS-TRAINING:

## NOTES

# TRAINING

## SEARCH YOUR
## SCHEDULE
· · · · · · ·

If you're finding it
difficult to make
time for running,
try to do it in short
30 minute bursts.
Set the alarm 30
minutes early, run
at while you're
waiting for your
children to finish
football practice,
or sneak in 30
minutes over
your lunch break.

### WEEKLY TOTAL

_____

### TOTAL MILEAGE TO DATE

_____

# WEEK 32

WEEK OF _____ TO_____

## TIP OF THE WEEK

Mix it up to curb boredom. If sitting on a stationary bike for half an hour is deadly dull compared to a run on your favourite trail, try cross-training with a different activity every 10 minutes. For example, do 10 minutes of cycling, then 10 minutes on the rowing machine, and finish up with 10 minutes on the elliptical trainer.

"Mind is everything; muscles, mere pieces of rubber. All that I am, I am because of my mind."

**Paavo Nurmi, nine-times Olympic track gold medallist**

### MONDAY
ROUTE:

DISTANCE:                     TIME:

NOTES:

CROSS-TRAINING:

### TUESDAY
ROUTE:

DISTANCE:                     TIME:

NOTES:

CROSS-TRAINING:

### WEDNESDAY
ROUTE:

DISTANCE:                     TIME:

NOTES:

CROSS-TRAINING:

### THURSDAY
ROUTE:

DISTANCE:                     TIME:

NOTES:

CROSS-TRAINING:

### FRIDAY
ROUTE:

DISTANCE:                     TIME:

NOTES:

CROSS-TRAINING:

## SATURDAY

ROUTE:

DISTANCE:                          TIME:

NOTES:

CROSS-TRAINING:

## SUNDAY

ROUTE:

DISTANCE:                          TIME:

NOTES:

CROSS-TRAINING:

## NOTES

# TRAINING

### BUSY SCHEDULE?

Ensure you are prepared for any opportunity to run. When training takes a backseat to all of the other things you have to do, just keep a bag of emergency workout gear in your car. Then, before you go home, after finishing errands, change into your running clothes and swing by the nearest park or trail.

### WEEKLY TOTAL

_____

### TOTAL MILEAGE TO DATE

_____

# TIP OF THE WEEK

To increase mileage without risking shin splints, try pool running. Do a water workout on an interval day to build mileage or in place of your regular workout.

"A lot of people run a race to see who's the fastest. I run to see who has the most guts."

**Steve Prefontaine, one-time holder of seven US track records from 2000m to 10,000m**

## MONDAY

ROUTE:

DISTANCE:                    TIME:

NOTES:

CROSS-TRAINING:

## TUESDAY

ROUTE:

DISTANCE:                    TIME:

NOTES:

CROSS-TRAINING:

## WEDNESDAY

ROUTE:

DISTANCE:                    TIME:

NOTES:

CROSS-TRAINING:

## THURSDAY

ROUTE:

DISTANCE:                    TIME:

NOTES:

CROSS-TRAINING:

## FRIDAY

ROUTE:

DISTANCE:                    TIME:

NOTES:

CROSS-TRAINING:

## SATURDAY

ROUTE:

DISTANCE:                    TIME:

NOTES:

CROSS-TRAINING:

## SUNDAY

ROUTE:

DISTANCE:                    TIME:

NOTES:

CROSS-TRAINING:

## NOTES

# TRAINING

## CORE BUILDER
· · · · · · ·

To prevent injuries that can stem from a forward tilt of the pelvis while you are running, try some stabilisation exercises that focus on your abs. One favourite is called the quadruped: start on all fours, raise your left arm and right leg until they are parallel with the ground. Hold for two seconds, lower, and repeat with your right arm and left leg. Repeat 8-10 times on each side.

### WEEKLY TOTAL

### TOTAL MILEAGE TO DATE

## TIP OF THE WEEK

To prevent injuries such as muscle strains, curb your urge to lengthen your stride at the end of a long run. Use more of a shuffle when you get tired. Quicken the turnover of these short strides to keep your pace steady.

"Learn to run when feeling the pain: then push harder."

**William Sigei, former 10,000m world record holder**

### MONDAY
ROUTE:

DISTANCE:                    TIME:

NOTES:


CROSS-TRAINING:

### TUESDAY
ROUTE:

DISTANCE:                    TIME:

NOTES:


CROSS-TRAINING:

### WEDNESDAY
ROUTE:

DISTANCE:                    TIME:

NOTES:


CROSS-TRAINING:

### THURSDAY
ROUTE:

DISTANCE:                    TIME:

NOTES:


CROSS-TRAINING:

### FRIDAY
ROUTE:

DISTANCE:                    TIME:

NOTES:


CROSS-TRAINING:

## SATURDAY

ROUTE:

DISTANCE:                          TIME:

NOTES:

CROSS-TRAINING:

## SUNDAY

ROUTE:

DISTANCE:                          TIME:

NOTES:

CROSS-TRAINING:

## NOTES

# NUTRITION

### SKIP THE SWEETS

Beat your post-workout sweet tooth and avoid an after-run junk-food binge by never training on empty. Take in at least 400 to 600 calories about two hours before a run. If you're going out longer than 90 minutes, carry a snack with you.

## WEEKLY TOTAL

_____

## TOTAL MILEAGE TO DATE

_____

# WEEK 35

WEEK OF _____ TO _____

## TIP OF THE WEEK

Set two goals for a race. One primary and one secondary 'bad-day back-up'. Then, if things don't go right on race day – and they often don't – you can focus on the alternative aim. Your primary goal is the one you've been working towards: running a personal best, beating your rival, whatever. Your secondary goal should keep you motivated when you're having a bad day: slowing down only over the second half – or just reaching the finish line.

"Stadiums are for spectators. We runners have nature, and that is much better."

**Juha Väätäinen, double European Championship track gold medallist**

### MONDAY
ROUTE:

DISTANCE:                TIME:

NOTES:

CROSS-TRAINING:

### TUESDAY
ROUTE:

DISTANCE:                TIME:

NOTES:

CROSS-TRAINING:

### WEDNESDAY
ROUTE:

DISTANCE:                TIME:

NOTES:

CROSS-TRAINING:

### THURSDAY
ROUTE:

DISTANCE:                TIME:

NOTES:

CROSS-TRAINING:

### FRIDAY
ROUTE:

DISTANCE:                TIME:

NOTES:

CROSS-TRAINING:

## SATURDAY

ROUTE:

DISTANCE:                    TIME:

NOTES:

CROSS-TRAINING:

## SUNDAY

ROUTE:

DISTANCE:                    TIME:

NOTES:

CROSS-TRAINING:

## NOTES

# TRAINING

## IF THE SHOE FITS...

Be sure to run in new trainers before a race. Trying to prevent blisters, especially in a marathon, may seem like a futile attempt. But buying new race shoes and wearing them for at least one 10-mile run at marathon pace can determine where your sore spots will be. If the shoes bother you, get another pair.

**WEEKLY TOTAL**

**TOTAL MILEAGE TO DATE**

# WEEK 36

**WEEK OF** _____ TO _____

## MONDAY
ROUTE:

DISTANCE:                    TIME:

NOTES:

CROSS-TRAINING:

## TUESDAY
ROUTE:

DISTANCE:                    TIME:

NOTES:

CROSS-TRAINING:

## WEDNESDAY
ROUTE:

DISTANCE:                    TIME:

NOTES:

CROSS-TRAINING:

## THURSDAY
ROUTE:

DISTANCE:                    TIME:

NOTES:

CROSS-TRAINING:

## FRIDAY
ROUTE:

DISTANCE:                    TIME:

NOTES:

CROSS-TRAINING:

## SATURDAY

ROUTE:

DISTANCE:                    TIME:

NOTES:

CROSS-TRAINING:

## SUNDAY

ROUTE:

DISTANCE:                    TIME:

NOTES:

CROSS-TRAINING:

## NOTES

# TRAINING

## STEADY THE PACE

· · · · · · ·

A treadmill will help you run steady because you can keep it going at the same speed the whole run. Or teach your body to conserve energy by upping the speed in the last half of the workout.

### WEEKLY TOTAL

### TOTAL MILEAGE TO DATE

## TIP OF THE WEEK

Help speed your leg turnover by wearing lightweight running shoes when you hop on a treadmill. The superior cushioning on the machine lets you get away with flimsier footwear during long workouts, and you'll be a more efficient runner without the extra weight.

"Get out well, but not too quickly. Move through the field, be comfortable. Go with your strengths. If you don't have a great finish, you must get away to win."

**John Treacy,
cross-country running
world champion**

### MONDAY
ROUTE:

DISTANCE:                          TIME:

NOTES:

CROSS-TRAINING:

### TUESDAY
ROUTE:

DISTANCE:                          TIME:

NOTES:

CROSS-TRAINING:

### WEDNESDAY
ROUTE:

DISTANCE:                          TIME:

NOTES:

CROSS-TRAINING:

### THURSDAY
ROUTE:

DISTANCE:                          TIME:

NOTES:

CROSS-TRAINING:

### FRIDAY
ROUTE:

DISTANCE:                          TIME:

NOTES:

CROSS-TRAINING:

## SATURDAY
ROUTE:

DISTANCE:                TIME:

NOTES:

CROSS-TRAINING:

## SUNDAY
ROUTE:

DISTANCE:                TIME:

NOTES:

CROSS-TRAINING:

## NOTES

# TRAINING

## MENTAL RUNNING
· · · · · ·

Move past a bad day – just ignore it. The best way to recover from a bad run is to forget about it and not obsess or ask yourself, "What if?" Cut the workout short, or take it easy on your next run. Stay positive, and know that the good days will always outweigh the bad.

### WEEKLY TOTAL

### TOTAL MILEAGE TO DATE

# WEEK 38

WEEK OF _____ TO _____

## TIP OF THE WEEK

Speed up for the last 600 metres of a race. It can be hard to pick up the pace once you've settled into a set rhythm. To speed things up, but in a controlled manner, try this workout: Run 400 meters at a comfortable pace, followed by 200 meters at one-mile race pace. Repeat three to five times with three minutes' recovery.

"I don't drink. I don't kiss girls. These things do an athlete in."

**Suleiman Nyambui, twice winner of the Berlin Marathon**

### MONDAY
ROUTE:

DISTANCE:                    TIME:

NOTES:

CROSS-TRAINING:

### TUESDAY
ROUTE:

DISTANCE:                    TIME:

NOTES:

CROSS-TRAINING:

### WEDNESDAY
ROUTE:

DISTANCE:                    TIME:

NOTES:

CROSS-TRAINING:

### THURSDAY
ROUTE:

DISTANCE:                    TIME:

NOTES:

CROSS-TRAINING:

### FRIDAY
ROUTE:

DISTANCE:                    TIME:

NOTES:

CROSS-TRAINING:

## SATURDAY

ROUTE:

DISTANCE:                    TIME:

NOTES:

CROSS-TRAINING:

## SUNDAY

ROUTE:

DISTANCE:                    TIME:

NOTES:

CROSS-TRAINING:

## NOTES

# TRAINING

### ICE, ICE BABY
· · · · · · ·

Make an ice bag with three parts water to one part rubbing alcohol. Alcohol freezes at a significantly lower temperature than water does, so the pack is colder but still liquid. Place a towel or washcloth between your skin and the pack to protect your skin.

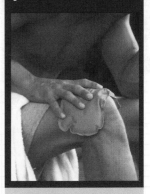

## WEEKLY TOTAL

_____

## TOTAL MILEAGE TO DATE

_____

## TIP OF THE WEEK

To make sure you're training at the right level of intensity, pick up a heart-rate monitor. Long runs should be at 70 to 80 percent maximum heart rate, tempo runs at 80 to 90 percent maximum heart-rate, and intervals from 90 to 100 percent maximum.

"If you want to win a race, you have to go a little berserk."

**Bill Rodgers, former holder of the US marathon record**

### MONDAY
ROUTE:

DISTANCE:                     TIME:

NOTES:

CROSS-TRAINING:

### TUESDAY
ROUTE:

DISTANCE:                     TIME:

NOTES:

CROSS-TRAINING:

### WEDNESDAY
ROUTE:

DISTANCE:                     TIME:

NOTES:

CROSS-TRAINING:

### THURSDAY
ROUTE:

DISTANCE:                     TIME:

NOTES:

CROSS-TRAINING:

### FRIDAY
ROUTE:

DISTANCE:                     TIME:

NOTES:

CROSS-TRAINING:

## SATURDAY

ROUTE:

DISTANCE:                          TIME:

NOTES:

CROSS-TRAINING:

## SUNDAY

ROUTE:

DISTANCE:                          TIME:

NOTES:

CROSS-TRAINING:

## NOTES

# TRAINING
## LANDMARK
## ACHIEVEMENTS
· · · · · · ·
Use landmarks to solve pacing problems. If you start out too fast on runs, map out a route, and time yourself against particular points. Slow down the early segments of your next runs until you feel strong the whole way round.

| WEEKLY TOTAL |
| --- |
| |

| TOTAL MILEAGE TO DATE |
| --- |
| |

# WEEK 40

WEEK OF _____ TO _____

## TIP OF THE WEEK

Successful speed training is built upon strong aerobic conditioning. Before adding speed workouts, prepare your body with several weeks or even a few months of longer runs, plus a smattering of tempo running or hill work.

"Those who say that I will lose and am finished will have to run over my body to beat me."

**Said Aouita, Olympic 5000m gold medallist**

### MONDAY
ROUTE:

DISTANCE:                    TIME:

NOTES:

CROSS-TRAINING:

### TUESDAY
ROUTE:

DISTANCE:                    TIME:

NOTES:

CROSS-TRAINING:

### WEDNESDAY
ROUTE:

DISTANCE:                    TIME:

NOTES:

CROSS-TRAINING:

### THURSDAY
ROUTE:

DISTANCE:                    TIME:

NOTES:

CROSS-TRAINING:

### FRIDAY
ROUTE:

DISTANCE:                    TIME:

NOTES:

CROSS-TRAINING:

## SATURDAY

ROUTE:

DISTANCE:                    TIME:

NOTES:

CROSS-TRAINING:

## SUNDAY

ROUTE:

DISTANCE:                    TIME:

NOTES:

CROSS-TRAINING:

## NOTES

# NUTRITION

## OLIVE OIL KNOW-HOW

Preserve the disease-fighting antioxidants in olive oil by always keeping it in a cool, dark cupboard, and purchase it in quantities you'll use within a year. After this time antioxidants will break down.

### WEEKLY TOTAL

_____

### TOTAL MILEAGE TO DATE

_____

# WEEK 41

WEEK OF _____ TO _____

## TIP OF THE WEEK

Keep your feet light (and mentally prepare to go fast) by strapping on a pair of flat soled or lightweight running shoes when doing speed workouts. This works best for repeats below 800 meters.

"It is a paradox to say the human body has no limit. There must be a limit to the speed at which men can run. I feel this may be around 3:30 for the mile. However, another paradox remains – if an athlete manages to run 3:30, another runner could be found to marginally improve on that time."

**Roger Bannister, first to run a four-minute mile**

### MONDAY
ROUTE:

DISTANCE:                    TIME:

NOTES:

CROSS-TRAINING:

### TUESDAY
ROUTE:

DISTANCE:                    TIME:

NOTES:

CROSS-TRAINING:

### WEDNESDAY
ROUTE:

DISTANCE:                    TIME:

NOTES:

CROSS-TRAINING:

### THURSDAY
ROUTE:

DISTANCE:                    TIME:

NOTES:

CROSS-TRAINING:

### FRIDAY
ROUTE:

DISTANCE:                    TIME:

NOTES:

CROSS-TRAINING:

## SATURDAY
ROUTE:

DISTANCE:                    TIME:

NOTES:

CROSS-TRAINING:

## SUNDAY
ROUTE:

DISTANCE:                    TIME:

NOTES:

CROSS-TRAINING:

## NOTES

# TRAINING

### X-TRAIN
·······

Cross-train to build stamina while giving your body a rest. It's a good way to up fitness without pounding your legs. Choose non-weight-bearing activities, such as pool running or rowing. Cross-training is also a great way to recover from an injury.

**WEEKLY TOTAL**

_____

**TOTAL MILEAGE TO DATE**

_____

## TIP OF THE WEEK

Stabilise the core muscles, which are important for running posture, by using a stability ball. Almost any basic strength-training exercise – crunches, bicep curls – can be done on a stability ball to add an extra balance challenge or additional resistance.

"The only tactics I admire are do-or-die."

**Herb Elliot, Olympic 1500m gold medallist**

### MONDAY
ROUTE:

DISTANCE:                         TIME:

NOTES:

CROSS-TRAINING:

### TUESDAY
ROUTE:

DISTANCE:                         TIME:

NOTES:

CROSS-TRAINING:

### WEDNESDAY
ROUTE:

DISTANCE:                         TIME:

NOTES:

CROSS-TRAINING:

### THURSDAY
ROUTE:

DISTANCE:                         TIME:

NOTES:

CROSS-TRAINING:

### FRIDAY
ROUTE:

DISTANCE:                         TIME:

NOTES:

CROSS-TRAINING:

## SATURDAY

ROUTE:

DISTANCE:                    TIME:

NOTES:

CROSS-TRAINING:

## SUNDAY

ROUTE:

DISTANCE:                    TIME:

NOTES:

CROSS-TRAINING:

## NOTES

# NUTRITION

## BURN FAT
· · · · · · ·
If one of your aims is to burn fat, try a morning run before breakfast. Low glycogen stores mean your body will break down fat for energy. However, make sure you keep your pace easy (around 65% of your maximum heart rate) otherwise you risk cannibalising your muscle tissue for energy, too.

### WEEKLY TOTAL

### TOTAL MILEAGE TO DATE

# WEEK 43

WEEK OF _____ TO _____

## TIP OF THE WEEK

Training hard but can't seem to improve your times? It's called a training plateau, and it comes from doing too much of the same type of activity. A good starting point to get out of it: do one run a week further than your current limit, and run it slower than you usually run. Do this once a week for three weeks, each time adding a mile to your longest run.

"World records are only borrowed."

**Sebastian Coe, who set eight outdoor and three indoor world records in middle-distance running**

### MONDAY
ROUTE:

DISTANCE:                              TIME:

NOTES:

CROSS-TRAINING:

### TUESDAY
ROUTE:

DISTANCE:                              TIME:

NOTES:

CROSS-TRAINING:

### WEDNESDAY
ROUTE:

DISTANCE:                              TIME:

NOTES:

CROSS-TRAINING:

### THURSDAY
ROUTE:

DISTANCE:                              TIME:

NOTES:

CROSS-TRAINING:

### FRIDAY
ROUTE:

DISTANCE:                              TIME:

NOTES:

CROSS-TRAINING:

## SATURDAY
ROUTE:

DISTANCE:                    TIME:

NOTES:

CROSS-TRAINING:

## SUNDAY
ROUTE:

DISTANCE:                    TIME:

NOTES:

CROSS-TRAINING:

## NOTES

# TRAINING
## DOUBLE DUTY
· · · · · · ·
Do a double workout to beat the heat. If you're getting too hot on summer runs, split your mileage into two runs, one in the morning and one at night. You'll build up less body heat this way.

## WEEKLY TOTAL

## TOTAL MILEAGE TO DATE

# WEEK 44

WEEK OF _____ TO _____

## TIP OF THE WEEK

Plan your runs to avoid dehydration. Running in the heat can be uncomfortable and dangerous, so run in the morning and take shady routes. Also, look for routes with stops for water. If you can't find any, do a few loops near your house and stop for water at home at every lap.

"Everybody and their mother knows you don't train hard on Friday, the day before a race. But a lot of runners will overtrain on Thursday if left on their own. Thursday is the most dangerous day of the week."

**Marty Stern, veteran US track coach**

### MONDAY
ROUTE:

DISTANCE:                    TIME:

NOTES:


CROSS-TRAINING:

### TUESDAY
ROUTE:

DISTANCE:                    TIME:

NOTES:


CROSS-TRAINING:

### WEDNESDAY
ROUTE:

DISTANCE:                    TIME:

NOTES:


CROSS-TRAINING:

### THURSDAY
ROUTE:

DISTANCE:                    TIME:

NOTES:


CROSS-TRAINING:

### FRIDAY
ROUTE:

DISTANCE:                    TIME:

NOTES:


CROSS-TRAINING:

## SATURDAY

ROUTE:

DISTANCE:                    TIME:

NOTES:



CROSS-TRAINING:

## SUNDAY

ROUTE:

DISTANCE:                    TIME:

NOTES:



CROSS-TRAINING:

## NOTES

# TRAINING

### SHORT-TERM GOALS FOR LONG-TERM SUCCESS
· · · · · · ·
If you're having trouble finding a goal that works for you, think short-term. Good goals are inspirational, but they're also achievable. Interim goals that you can celebrate regularly will help you achieve a bigger goal.

### WEEKLY TOTAL

_____

### TOTAL MILEAGE TO DATE

_____

## TIP OF THE WEEK

Eat breakfast at the right time to keep your stomach happy. Glycogen stores are low when you wake up, so replenish them with a banana and bagel or toast and a sports bar. Even if you have to get up at an ungodly hour, eat two to three hours before the start of a race, or you risk indigestion.

"It is true that speed kills. In distance running, it kills anyone who does not have it."

**Brooks Johnson, US Olympic track and field coach**

### MONDAY

ROUTE:

DISTANCE:                    TIME:

NOTES:

CROSS-TRAINING:

### TUESDAY

ROUTE:

DISTANCE:                    TIME:

NOTES:

CROSS-TRAINING:

### WEDNESDAY

ROUTE:

DISTANCE:                    TIME:

NOTES:

CROSS-TRAINING:

### THURSDAY

ROUTE:

DISTANCE:                    TIME:

NOTES:

CROSS-TRAINING:

### FRIDAY

ROUTE:

DISTANCE:                    TIME:

NOTES:

CROSS-TRAINING:

## SATURDAY

ROUTE:

DISTANCE:                          TIME:

NOTES:

CROSS-TRAINING:

## SUNDAY

ROUTE:

DISTANCE:                          TIME:

NOTES:

CROSS-TRAINING:

## NOTES

# TRAINING

### TOE JAM
· · · · · · ·

A black toenail occurs when repeated jamming of the toes against a shoe causes the nail to dislodge. It can happen when shoes are either too big or too small, so go to a speciality running-shoe store and have the salesperson make sure there's a thumb's width between the end of your longest toe and the front of the shoe. Also, trim your toenails straight across.

### WEEKLY TOTAL

_____

### TOTAL MILEAGE TO DATE

_____

## TIP OF THE WEEK

If you have a red sore spot on the top of your foot after a run, your shoelaces may be rubbing. Try this lacing technique to ease the pressure: when lacing up, skip the centre holes. Don't cross the laces over the centre, either; just keep them on each side to make an open 'O' across the middle of your foot. At the top, cross the laces, and tie as usual.

### MONDAY
ROUTE:

DISTANCE:                          TIME:

NOTES:


CROSS-TRAINING:

### TUESDAY
ROUTE:

DISTANCE:                          TIME:

NOTES:


CROSS-TRAINING:

### WEDNESDAY
ROUTE:

DISTANCE:                          TIME:

NOTES:


CROSS-TRAINING:

### THURSDAY
ROUTE:

DISTANCE:                          TIME:

NOTES:


CROSS-TRAINING:

### FRIDAY
ROUTE:

DISTANCE:                          TIME:

NOTES:


CROSS-TRAINING:

## SATURDAY

ROUTE:

DISTANCE:                    TIME:

NOTES:

CROSS-TRAINING:

## SUNDAY

ROUTE:

DISTANCE:                    TIME:

NOTES:

CROSS-TRAINING:

## NOTES

## TRAINING

### BREAK UP TREADMILL MONOTONY
· · · · · ·
Love the idea of pace training but find treadmills boring? Make a running playlist on your MP3 player. Include up-tempo and slow songs to match how fast you're running at the time.

"Act like a horse. Be dumb. Just run."

**Jumbo Elliott, US track and field coach who trained five Olympic gold winners**

### WEEKLY TOTAL

_____

### TOTAL MILEAGE TO DATE

_____

# TIP OF THE WEEK

Chat it up – use the 'talk test' to gauge your effort. Knowing whether you're exercising too hard is as easy as reciting the National Anthem. If you're huffing and puffing so much that you can't seem to get a word out, you're overexerting. Unless you're doing interval training, slow down to where you're working hard but can still carry on a conversation.

"The 'talk test' was the greatest news I'd heard since I found out it was okay to eat pasta. If you're out of breath, slow down. What a great deal!"

**George Wendt, US actor, famed for playing Norm in *Cheers***

## MONDAY
ROUTE:

DISTANCE:                TIME:

NOTES:

CROSS-TRAINING:

## TUESDAY
ROUTE:

DISTANCE:                TIME:

NOTES:

CROSS-TRAINING:

## WEDNESDAY
ROUTE:

DISTANCE:                TIME:

NOTES:

CROSS-TRAINING:

## THURSDAY
ROUTE:

DISTANCE:                TIME:

NOTES:

CROSS-TRAINING:

## FRIDAY
ROUTE:

DISTANCE:                TIME:

NOTES:

CROSS-TRAINING:

## SATURDAY

ROUTE:

DISTANCE:                    TIME:

NOTES:

CROSS-TRAINING:

## SUNDAY

ROUTE:

DISTANCE:                    TIME:

NOTES:

CROSS-TRAINING:

## NOTES

# NUTRITION

## SALAD FIRST?
·······
Lower your calorie
intake by eating
a salad of mainly
greens and low-
calorie veg before
dinner. A study
showed this type of
starter discourages
high-calorie binges,
possibly because
your stomach
registers volume
rather than number
of calories to
determine fullness.

### WEEKLY TOTAL

_____

### TOTAL MILEAGE TO DATE

_____

## TIP OF THE WEEK

Novice and slower marathoners should use the first few miles of the race as a warm-up, easing into their goal pace. Only sub-four-hour marathoners should jog before the race, and for no more than 15 minutes.

"The marathon can humble you."

**Bill Rodgers, former holder of the US marathon record**

### MONDAY
ROUTE:

DISTANCE:                    TIME:

NOTES:


CROSS-TRAINING:

### TUESDAY
ROUTE:

DISTANCE:                    TIME:

NOTES:


CROSS-TRAINING:

### WEDNESDAY
ROUTE:

DISTANCE:                    TIME:

NOTES:


CROSS-TRAINING:

### THURSDAY
ROUTE:

DISTANCE:                    TIME:

NOTES:


CROSS-TRAINING:

### FRIDAY
ROUTE:

DISTANCE:                    TIME:

NOTES:


CROSS-TRAINING:

## SATURDAY
ROUTE:

DISTANCE:                    TIME:

NOTES:

CROSS-TRAINING:

## SUNDAY
ROUTE:

DISTANCE:                    TIME:

NOTES:

CROSS-TRAINING:

## NOTES

# TRAINING

## TAKE IT SLOW
· · · · · ·
Stop straining your body – increase intensity gradually. Faster running places greater strain on the body, which means muscles work harder and suffer more damage. To prevent this from being a problem, make intense workouts – hills, intervals, tempo runs – no more than 20 percent of your training. Never add more than one of these elements to your training at a time.

### WEEKLY TOTAL

### TOTAL MILEAGE TO DATE

# WEEK 49

WEEK OF _____ TO _____

## TIP OF THE WEEK

A long, hot shower after a race? Only if you want to be sore and creaky the next day. One of the best recovery methods is to slip into an ice bath for 5-10 minutes. You can make one at home simply by filling your tub with cold water. The latest studies prove that 10°C is the ideal temperature for ice baths, so you don't actually need to put any ice in them at all. Your cold tap at home has an average temperature of 7°C.

"Our greatest glory is not in never falling but in rising every time we fall."
**Confucius, philosopher**

### MONDAY
ROUTE:

DISTANCE:                    TIME:

NOTES:


CROSS-TRAINING:

### TUESDAY
ROUTE:

DISTANCE:                    TIME:

NOTES:


CROSS-TRAINING:

### WEDNESDAY
ROUTE:

DISTANCE:                    TIME:

NOTES:


CROSS-TRAINING:

### THURSDAY
ROUTE:

DISTANCE:                    TIME:

NOTES:


CROSS-TRAINING:

### FRIDAY
ROUTE:

DISTANCE:                    TIME:

NOTES:


CROSS-TRAINING:

## SATURDAY

ROUTE:

DISTANCE:                    TIME:

NOTES:

CROSS-TRAINING:

## SUNDAY

ROUTE:

DISTANCE:                    TIME:

NOTES:

CROSS-TRAINING:

## NOTES

# TRAINING

## BLOCK THE SUN
· · · · · · ·

It's important to prevent burns and skin cancer by slathering up in the sun – no doubt about it. But who wants to reapply during a run? Use a high-SPF formula, and apply an hour before heading out so that you won't have to interrupt a run or risk UV rays.

### WEEKLY TOTAL

### TOTAL MILEAGE TO DATE

## TIP OF THE WEEK

Recover easier: keep moving. To move blood through the body and jump-start recovery after a marathon, don't keel over at the finish line. Grab a cup of water and walk for at least half a mile.

"Sometimes, when I walk out onto the track I think, 'Why do I put myself through this?' But that's when you really get into your focus... you focus on the race you are going to run."

**Dame Kelly Holmes, double Olympic track gold medallist**

### MONDAY
ROUTE:

DISTANCE:                    TIME:

NOTES:

CROSS-TRAINING:

### TUESDAY
ROUTE:

DISTANCE:                    TIME:

NOTES:

CROSS-TRAINING:

### WEDNESDAY
ROUTE:

DISTANCE:                    TIME:

NOTES:

CROSS-TRAINING:

### THURSDAY
ROUTE:

DISTANCE:                    TIME:

NOTES:

CROSS-TRAINING:

### FRIDAY
ROUTE:

DISTANCE:                    TIME:

NOTES:

CROSS-TRAINING:

## SATURDAY
ROUTE:
DISTANCE:                TIME:
NOTES:


CROSS-TRAINING:

## SUNDAY
ROUTE:
DISTANCE:                TIME:
NOTES:


CROSS-TRAINING:

## NOTES

# TRAINING
## ACCELERATE
· · · · · ·
If your runs start out slow, only to end up at lightning pace, try a speed interval workout. Once a week, after a 10-minute warm-up, run a little faster for 30 seconds. Then walk for 30 seconds. Repeat two or three times. Each time, increase the pace a little bit. Each week, add two more bursts until you get to 10.

### WEEKLY TOTAL

_____

### TOTAL MILEAGE TO DATE

_____

# WEEK 51

WEEK OF _____ TO _____

## TIP OF THE WEEK

Recover faster by walking or jogging slowly the day after a marathon, even if you don't feel like it. It'll get the blood pumping through your legs again.

"Ask yourself: 'Can I give more?'. The answer is usually: 'Yes'."

**Paul Tergat, marathon world-record holder 2003-2007**

## MONDAY

ROUTE:

DISTANCE:        TIME:

NOTES:

CROSS-TRAINING:

## TUESDAY

ROUTE:

DISTANCE:        TIME:

NOTES:

CROSS-TRAINING:

## WEDNESDAY

ROUTE:

DISTANCE:        TIME:

NOTES:

CROSS-TRAINING:

## THURSDAY

ROUTE:

DISTANCE:        TIME:

NOTES:

CROSS-TRAINING:

## FRIDAY

ROUTE:

DISTANCE:        TIME:

NOTES:

CROSS-TRAINING:

## SATURDAY

ROUTE:

DISTANCE:                    TIME:

NOTES:

CROSS-TRAINING:

## SUNDAY

ROUTE:

DISTANCE:                    TIME:

NOTES:

CROSS-TRAINING:

## NOTES

# TRAINING

### SPRING TRAINING
·······

To teach your muscles to blast off the ground with greater force, try plyometrics. To do a vertical jump stand with feet hip-width apart, bend knees, and jump as high in the air as you can. Bend knees upon landing to absorb the impact.

### WEEKLY TOTAL

_____

### TOTAL MILEAGE TO DATE

_____

## TIP OF THE WEEK

Strength is key for the half-marathon, so train with hill repetitions and by running a hilly route on some of your medium-distance runs. The only time you won't want to do a lot of hills is if the course is completely flat. That means you'll have to use the same muscles the whole time, so hill workouts should be limited to once a week at most.

"I just had to get to the line first. My coach said, 'Get to the front with 600 meters left, and stay there.' I did."

**Lasse Viren, four-times Olympic track gold medallist**

### MONDAY
ROUTE:

DISTANCE:                              TIME:

NOTES:


CROSS-TRAINING:

### TUESDAY
ROUTE:

DISTANCE:                              TIME:

NOTES:


CROSS-TRAINING:

### WEDNESDAY
ROUTE:

DISTANCE:                              TIME:

NOTES:


CROSS-TRAINING:

### THURSDAY
ROUTE:

DISTANCE:                              TIME:

NOTES:


CROSS-TRAINING:

### FRIDAY
ROUTE:

DISTANCE:                              TIME:

NOTES:


CROSS-TRAINING:

## SATURDAY

ROUTE:

DISTANCE:                          TIME:

NOTES:

CROSS-TRAINING:

## SUNDAY

ROUTE:

DISTANCE:                          TIME:

NOTES:

CROSS-TRAINING:

## NOTES

# TRAINING

### TALK YOUR WAY FASTER
· · · · · · ·

Have a mantra you can use during a run to motivate yourself. Studies show that if you repeat a positive phrase to yourself, such as, "I'm running fast and strong", it will have a positive effect on your performance. It will also serve as a useful distraction from the exertion.

### WEEKLY TOTAL

### TOTAL MILEAGE TO DATE

## NOW WHAT?

**YOU'VE COME TO THE END OF THIS TRAINING DIARY. SO WHAT DO YOU DO NEXT?**

**C**ongratulations. You've reached the end of your running year. Now it's time for a quick review.

Maybe you ran every day of the past 52 weeks. Most likely you didn't. While some trail blazers manage to run 365 days a year, year after year, few of us follow suit. And that's a good thing. Neither Olympic coaches nor medical experts recommend an obsessive commitment to daily running.

The more important thing is reaching your goals. Ah, goals. So tantalising. So easy to set. So difficult to achieve.

This isn't the place for a treatise on setting goals, except to say they should be specific, realistic, meaningful, and wide-ranging. Don't focus exclusively on your training mileage and race times. Take a broader approach, one that considers health and motivation.

For example, aim to lose 10 pounds through a combination of better training and improved eating habits. Decide to enter a spring 10K and an autumn half-marathon, the better to focus your year-round training. Resolve to find several new training partners; they'll drag you along on those days when you don't feel like running.

How are you going to reach these goals? By using this training journal as your number one friend, motivator, and coach—especially at the end of the year. Here's how.

**1** Look back to your best race during the year. It wasn't a fluke. In running, there's no such thing as a 'lucky' day. You did something right — probably weeks and months of somethings. List them, and save the list.

**2** Find the four-week period when you ran the most miles. Try to figure out why this period worked so well for you. Why were others less successful? Copy the positive; eliminate the negative.

**3** Trace the course of any injuries you had during the year. Which came from accidents? Which from training mistakes? Don't make the same mistakes twice.

**4** Find the week or season of your healthiest weight. How did you get there? Your body weight is a key factor in both your health and your running success. The more you can control it, the better you'll feel and perform.

**5** Try to determine at what time of day you run the best. We're all biological creatures with a certain amount of preset wiring – are you a night owl who likes to sleep late, or are you up at the crack of dawn? You can fight your wiring. Or you can adapt to it and make it a strength.

**6** Show your diary to someone else; a coach, perhaps, or simply a more experienced runner friend. Either will be able to point out things that you'll probably miss.

**7** Make a seasonal, year-long plan for the next 12 months. You can't know what's going to happen to you in the coming year, but you'll have a better chance of achieving your running and fitness goals if you choose the basic path you hope to follow.

**8** Add at least one new exercise to your workout repertoire. Start strength training. Buy a mountain bike. Learn to swim. Consider cross-country skiing. Every new workout gives a stronger foundation to your fitness programme.

**9** Pick several new races to enter in the coming year. The world of aerobic sports is exploding, and you don't have to eat ants during a 10-day death march in Sumatra to enjoy it. Try a trail race or a mountain race. Get a few friends together for a road relay. Or simply enter some races or race distances you've never tackled before.

**10** Buy another training diary. Seriously, many studies have proven the power of writing things down. For a runner, that means a training diary. Don't get caught without one.

## SHOE HISTORY

### SHOES I WORE THIS YEAR AND WHY

You don't need a lot of gear to start running regularly or to enjoy it if you're a veteran. But you don't want to pinch pennies when you're shopping for running shoes, either. If the shoe fits, buy it. You don't want to run in shoes that don't fit perfectly—or that have too many miles on them. As a rule, we recommend replacing your shoes once you've done around 300 miles in them, fewer if you've abused them with mud, salt, or lots of puddles. Better yet, get two pairs of the same kind of running shoe and use them on alternate runs. It sometimes takes a few false starts to find the shoes that are right for you. We suggest you use the spaces below to record information on the shoes you use this year. It will help you find the style that's best for you.

DATE PURCHASED:

SHOE BRAND AND NAME:

SIZE:

WHERE YOU BOUGHT IT:

WAS YOUR FOOT SIZE MEASURED?

IF SO, WHAT SIZE WAS IT?

PRICE:

DATE YOU STARTED RUNNING IN THEM:

DATE THE SHOE WAS RETIRED FROM ACTIVE DUTY:

MILES OF USE:

IMPRESSIONS:

DATE PURCHASED:

SHOE BRAND AND NAME:

SIZE:

WHERE YOU BOUGHT IT:

WAS YOUR FOOT SIZE MEASURED?

IF SO, WHAT SIZE WAS IT?

PRICE:

DATE YOU STARTED RUNNING IN THEM:

DATE THE SHOE WAS RETIRED FROM ACTIVE DUTY:

MILES OF USE:

IMPRESSIONS:


DATE PURCHASED:

SHOE BRAND AND NAME:

SIZE:

WHERE YOU BOUGHT IT:

WAS YOUR FOOT SIZE MEASURED?

IF SO, WHAT SIZE WAS IT?

PRICE:

DATE YOU STARTED RUNNING IN THEM:

DATE THE SHOE WAS RETIRED FROM ACTIVE DUTY:

MILES OF USE:

IMPRESSIONS:

## RACE PERFORMANCE

### HOW I DID AT THE RACES

Whether you're a veteran road warrior or someone who's new to running, we suggest you run in at least six races a year. Racing is a great experience. You get to put yourself and your fitness to the test, you come together with the community of like-minded people who can say the word fartlek without giggling, and your training gains a focus. Besides, how else are you going to get T-shirts? Record your race performances in the spaces below, and have fun.

RACE NAME:

TOWN:

DISTANCE:

TIME:

DESCRIBE THE COURSE:

YOUR PLACE OVERALL:

AGE-GROUP PLACE:

DESCRIBE THE WHOLE EXPERIENCE:

RACE NAME:

TOWN:

DISTANCE:

TIME:

DESCRIBE THE COURSE:

YOUR PLACE OVERALL:

AGE-GROUP PLACE:

DESCRIBE THE WHOLE EXPERIENCE:

RACE NAME:

TOWN:

DISTANCE:

TIME:

DESCRIBE THE COURSE:

YOUR PLACE OVERALL:

AGE-GROUP PLACE:

DESCRIBE THE WHOLE EXPERIENCE:

RACE NAME:

TOWN:

DISTANCE:

TIME:

DESCRIBE THE COURSE:

YOUR PLACE OVERALL:

AGE-GROUP PLACE:

DESCRIBE THE WHOLE EXPERIENCE:

RACE NAME:

TOWN:

DISTANCE:

TIME:

DESCRIBE THE COURSE:

YOUR PLACE OVERALL:

AGE-GROUP PLACE:

DESCRIBE THE WHOLE EXPERIENCE:

RACE NAME:

TOWN:

DISTANCE:

TIME:

DESCRIBE THE COURSE:

YOUR PLACE OVERALL:

AGE-GROUP PLACE:

DESCRIBE THE WHOLE EXPERIENCE:

RACE NAME:

TOWN:

DISTANCE:

TIME:

DESCRIBE THE COURSE:

YOUR PLACE OVERALL:

AGE-GROUP PLACE:

DESCRIBE THE WHOLE EXPERIENCE:

---

RACE NAME:

TOWN:

DISTANCE:

TIME:

DESCRIBE THE COURSE:

YOUR PLACE OVERALL:

AGE-GROUP PLACE:

DESCRIBE THE WHOLE EXPERIENCE:

---

RACE NAME:

TOWN:

DISTANCE:

TIME:

DESCRIBE THE COURSE:

YOUR PLACE OVERALL:

AGE-GROUP PLACE:

DESCRIBE THE WHOLE EXPERIENCE:

## RAVE RUNS

## MILES WORTH OF MEMORIES

What makes a run memorable? The answers are as different as runners themselves. Maybe it's the weather. Maybe it's your companion and the conversation you have. Many problems have been solved during a run with a good partner. Maybe you achieve a goal such as a personal best on a regular course or more distance than you've done before. Maybe it's a combination of all the above, one of those ephemeral days when the universe aligns itself, and you run down a ribbon of gossamer that seems never-ending. We know a guy who claims that, for him, running is pure drudgery 90 percent of the time and pure joy 10 percent of the time, but it's the way he feels during the 10 percent that makes the 90 percent worth it. While we don't envy him his ratio, we understand the sentiment, and we encourage you to record this year's rave runs in the spaces provided below.

DATE:

ROUTE:

MILES:

TIME:

COMPANIONS:

DISCUSSION OR THOUGHTS:

WEATHER:

WHY WAS THIS RUN SO MEMORABLE?

DATE:

ROUTE:

MILES:

TIME:

COMPANIONS:

DISCUSSION OR THOUGHTS:

WEATHER:

WHY WAS THIS RUN SO MEMORABLE?

DATE:

ROUTE:

MILES:

TIME:

COMPANIONS:

DISCUSSION OR THOUGHTS:

WEATHER:

WHY WAS THIS RUN SO MEMORABLE?

DATE:

ROUTE:

MILES:

TIME:

COMPANIONS:

DISCUSSION OR THOUGHTS:

WEATHER:

WHY WAS THIS RUN SO MEMORABLE?

DATE:

ROUTE:

MILES:

TIME:

COMPANIONS:

DISCUSSION OR THOUGHTS:

WEATHER:

WHY WAS THIS RUN SO MEMORABLE?

DATE:

ROUTE:

MILES:

TIME:

COMPANIONS:

DISCUSSION OR THOUGHTS:

WEATHER:

WHY WAS THIS RUN SO MEMORABLE?

DATE:

ROUTE:

MILES:

TIME:

COMPANIONS:

DISCUSSION OR THOUGHTS:

WEATHER:

WHY WAS THIS RUN SO MEMORABLE?

## NOTES

## NOTES

_____
_____
_____
_____
_____
_____
_____
_____
_____
_____
_____
_____
_____
_____
_____
_____

## PHOTO CREDITS

11, 15, 67 - Studio 33

13 - Nick Pope

17 - Jon Witaker

22 - Dave Gratton

24, 27, 31, 104 - Runner's World

25 - Simon Keitch

40 - Leo Acker

43 - Helen Marsden

44 - Mike King

63 - Daniel Cottage

80 - Adrian Weinbrecht

All other images - Natmag-Rodale